STRESS, HEALTH
and Your Lifestyle

Lifeskills Personal Development Series

The series includes the following titles:

Assertiveness – A Positive Process
Communication – Time to Talk
Preparing for Successful Learning
Relationships – A Question of Quality
Stress, Health and Your Lifestyle
Successful Learning in Action
Time Management – Conquer the Clock
Transitions – The Challenge of Change

STRESS, HEALTH
and Your Lifestyle

John D. Adams

MERCURY

First published in 1989 by Lifeskills Publishing Group
New Edition published in 1993
by Mercury Business Books Ltd
125A The Broadway, Didcot, Oxfordshire OX11 8AW

Drawings by Kate Charlesworth

Typeset by Phoenix Photosetting, Chatham, Kent

Printed and bound in Great Britain by
Redwood Books, Trowbridge, Wilts

British Library Cataloguing in Publication Data is available

ISBN 1-85252-196-1

Foreword

Dear Reader,

Welcome to our series of open learning workbooks! In this brief foreword, we invite you to consider some of our beliefs:

- We do not need teachers to learn! Most of what we know in life was not learned in school, college or formal education. We can, and do, learn in a whole range of ways and we learn best when we know our own needs.

- The best way to help people is to encourage them to help themselves. Self-help and self-management avoid the dependency which blocks development and burdens ourselves and others.

- Awareness, knowledge and skills give us more options in life. Lack of any of these is a disadvantage; possession of them allows us to live fuller lives, shaping events rather than simply reacting.

- The more able and accomplished we become, the more we fill society's reservoir of talent and contribute to the common good.

The term 'lifeskill' came from work based on these beliefs which we began at Leeds University in the 1970s. Our philosophy has been widely applied in education, in industry and commerce, and in the community, inviting people to take charge of their lives and make them satisfying and rewarding.

Lifeskills have so far been available through training courses and teaching programmes. *Now* they are available in a self-help format consistent with the Lifeskills approach because *you* are in charge of your own learning. Learn at your own pace, in your own time, and apply your learning to your situation. We wish you both enjoyment and success!

Barrie Hopson

Mike Scally

November 1991

Before You Start...

This workbook has been written for people wanting to know more about personal self-development. It is about reading and doing, so we have chosen to write it as an open learning workbook.

What is open learning? Open learning is a term used to describe a study programme which is very flexibly designed so that it adapts to the needs of individual learners. Some open learning programmes involve attendance at a study centre of some kind, or contact with a tutor or mentor, but even then attendance times are flexible and suit the individual. This workbook is for you to use at home or at work and most of the activities are for you to complete alone. We sometimes suggest that it would be helpful to talk with a friend or colleague – self development is easier if there is another person with whom to talk over ideas. But this isn't essential by any means.

With this workbook you can:

- organise your study to suit your own needs

- study the material alone or with other people

- work through the book at your own pace

- start and finish just where and when you want to, although we have indicated some suggested stopping points with a symbol

Contents

Section One: Stress and How It Affects You

One factor which we hear about increasingly in relation to health is *stress*. But what exactly is stress and how does it manifest itself? What can we do to protect ourselves against too much or too little stress? The aims of this workbook are:

- To establish the causes of stress and strain.

- To identify stress-inducing situations.

- To provide you with an opportunity to assess your present stress levels.

- To give you a 'snapshot' of how your current lifestyle and behaviour may be affecting your 'health account'.

- To provide some guidelines and ideas for improving your health and stress ratings.

- To help you create a realistic action plan for better health and stress management.

A certain amount of stress can spur us into action and stimulate us to produce better work. Too much stress, however, can reduce our capabilities and have a harmful effect on our general well-being.

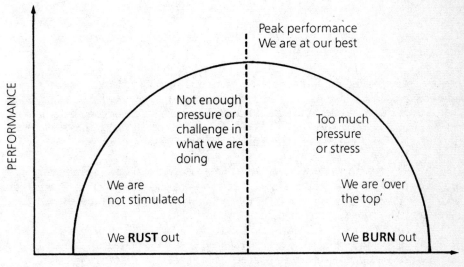

Excessive stress can be very costly to both our health and our daily activities. Our response to stress is a primitive biological response, which has not changed since the Stone Age. This response, known as the Fight or Flight Response, evolved to help our ancestors cope with threats and crises. Our bodies still react as if we were running away from a sabre-toothed tiger or preparing to fight an enemy from another tribe! These reactions are no longer really necessary or suitable in most modern stressful situations, so we bottle them up. This stored fight or flight readiness eventually causes *strain*.

The stress response itself is triggered by the autonomic nervous system, and is sustained by the endocrine glands (principally the thyroid and the adrenal glands). These systems ordinarily keep us in balance, but when we see something as stressful, they create a new equilibrium which prepares us for quick action. As the strain builds up, performance declines and the risk to health increases.

Strain puts every system in the body under pressure, eventually causing weak links to break or collapse. Everyone has some systems which are weaker than others, but these vary enormously from person to person. Can you suggest why some people are more prone to ill health than others?

....

....

....

....

....

Risk Factors

Factors which can affect the way our bodies react include hereditary factors, previous illness, accidents, personality and lifestyle habits. It is impossible to say which illnesses could be caused by excessive stress, but there is no doubt that stress is a major contributor to many illnesses that people experience. There are, of course, plenty of risks to health which are beyond our control, but many factors can be controlled by the individual.

Research has shown that approximately 18% of the total risks to the average person's health are biological, i.e. hereditary or due to accidents, previous illnesses and abuses. There is little you can do to remove these biological factors, although you should be aware of them and if necessary take the relevant precautions.

A further 18% of the total risks to health arise from environmental factors, including pollution, noise, over-crowding, etc. These can be changed but most of the changes need widespread political and social support to be effective.

Approximately 10% of health risks come from health care itself, through wrong diagnoses, drug side-effects, secondary infections and so on. This leaves a massive 54% of overall risks which are a result of controllable lifestyle choices. Jot down here what you think some of these lifestyle choices may be.

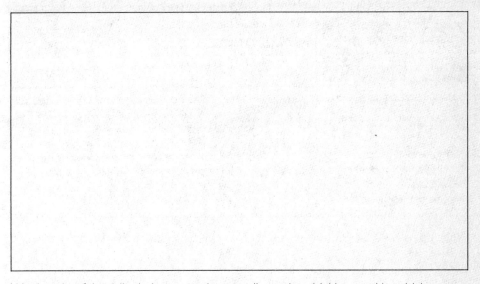

We thought of the daily choices we make regarding eating, drinking, smoking, driving, exercising, etc. Poor lifestyle habits and stress are likely to produce degenerative illnesses, such as ulcers, cardiovascular disease, back problems, forms of cancer and arthritis. If you can control these lifestyle factors, you can significantly increase your chances of protecting your health, and improving your performance.

It is now well established that our persistent patterns of thinking and the daily choices we make have a very great deal to do with the level of our physical and mental well-being. We believe that people who expect to be healthy, and have positive, moderate and confident outlooks are generally healthier than those who have negative, pessimistic and unconfident attitudes to life. Write down any thoughts you have about this.

....

....

....

Those people who avoid the known risks and engage in activities which are known to promote health are generally more healthy than those people who ignore the warnings and do little to look after themselves. There are of course exceptions: we all know the anecdotes about Grandpa who still smokes 80 cigarettes a day! On the next page are some people's reactions to ideas about healthy living.

> I didn't take any notice of what I ate until I began to put a bit of weight on. I'm really careful now, and find that I enjoy eating healthily.

> I know that stress affects me .... I get bad headaches and stomach pains. I try to take regular exercise and that helps me to feel better.

> WELL, I DON'T KNOW! MY MUM SMOKES 40 A DAY, NEVER DOES ANY EXERCISE AND EATS CHIPS LIKE THEY'RE GOING OUT OF FASHION – BUT SHE'S NEVER HAD A DAY'S ILLNESS IN HER LIFE!

Write down any 'yes, buts', reservations or comments about healthy living in the space below.

....

....

The fundamental issue is one of self-responsibility – if you don't take charge of looking after yourself, who will? To maintain good health, high energy and vitality, even under stressful conditions, requires you to be in charge of your life. *You can choose to be healthy.*

The next part of this workbook will provide you with a variety of questionnaires, each dealing with a certain aspect of health and lifestyle habits. After each questionnaire, you will be able to assess your results and read the background information which gives you practical advice on how to improve your rating. We hope that the act of filling in the questionnaires will in itself stimulate you to think more deeply about what you could be doing to manage the pressures of your life better, and to improve your overall health.

When you have completed the questionnaires and read the advice, you will have the most up-to-date information we are able to provide on your present levels of stress. You will also be aware of the controllable risks to your health and be equipped with tips and suggestions on how to reduce those risks.

Section Two: Changes At Work And Elsewhere

Changes At Work

The following list contains many of the episodes or events which have been found to cause stress in people in the course of their daily work. For each of the events on the following list which *has happened* to you during the past year, copy the *adjustment score* on to the line in the *did happen* column.

When you have done that, think about whether or not the event in question had a *high impact* on your stress level. For example, the event may have left you shocked, or unsure of what to do next. If you judge this to have had a high impact on you copy the *adjustment score* on to the line in the *high impact* column (this is in addition to entering it in the *did happen* column).

EVENT	ADJUSTMENT SCORE	DID HAPPEN	HIGH IMPACT
1 Transferred against your will to a new position or assignment	81		
2 Being shelved (moved to a less important job)	79		
3 Decrease in status (either actual or in relation to peers)	68		
4 Disciplined or seriously reprimanded by your supervisor	67		
5 Rejection of your request to transfer to a new, more satisfying job	65		
6 Sudden significant change in the nature of your work	60		
7 Cancellation of a project you were involved with and considered important	60		
8 Major or frequent changes in instructions, policies or procedures	59		

EVENT	ADJUSTMENT SCORE	DID HAPPEN	HIGH IMPACT
9 Being promoted or advanced at a slower rate than you expected	58		
10 Transferred voluntarily to a new position (not a promotion)	52		
11 Anticipation of own imminent retirement	47		
12 Major reorganisation (at least department-wide)	46		
13 Sudden decrease in number of positive recognitions of your accomplishments from any source	46		
14 Major change of technology affecting your job	46		
15 Gave major briefing or formal presentation	46		
16 Significant deterioration in environmental conditions (lighting, noise, temperature, space, etc.)	45		
17 New boss or supervisor	45		
18 Sudden significant decrease in the activity level of your work	43		
19 Sudden significant increase in the activity level of your work	37		
20 Major relocation of your workplace	31		
21 Increase in status (either actual or in relation to your peers)	30		
22 Required to work more hours per week than normal due to deadlines, crises, etc.	29		

EVENT	ADJUSTMENT SCORE	DID HAPPEN	HIGH IMPACT
23 Transfer, resignation, or retirement of a close friend or valued colleague	24		
24 Being promoted or advanced at a faster rate than you expected	24		
25 New subordinates	23		
26 Major change in work schedule	23		
27 New co-workers	21		
28 Sudden increase in number of positive recognitions of accomplishments from any source at work	20		
29 Significant improvement in environmental conditions at work (lighting, noise, temperature, space, etc.)	17		
30 Minor relocation of workplace	5		
		TOTAL SCORE	HIGH IMPACT SCORE

Above items adapted from D Naismith, 'Stress among managers as a function of organis-ational change'. Unpublished doctoral dissertation, George Washington University, 1975. Used with permission.

Changes In Situation Away From Work

This section contains many of the episodes or events which have been found to cause stress reactions in people in their lives away from employment. For each of the events on the fol-lowing list which *has happened* to you in the last twelve months, copy the *adjustment score* on to the line in the *did happen* column. Then, consider whether or not each of these events which has happened to you had a *high impact* on you. For each of the events which had a high impact on your experience of stress, copy the *adjustment score* on to the line in the *high impact* column in addition to entering it in the *did happen* column.

EVENT	ADJUSTMENT SCORE	DID HAPPEN	HIGH IMPACT
1 Death of spouse	86		
2 Divorce/break-up of family	77		
3 Gaol sentence	75		
4 Marital separation	70		
5 Unwanted pregnancy	70		
6 Death of immediate family member	69		
7 Unemployment of head of household	68		
8 Immediate family member attempted suicide	66		
9 Getting into debt beyond means of repayment	66		
10 Immediate family member starts drinking heavily	65		
11 Miscarriage	65		
12 Serious illness or injury requiring hospitalisation	65		
13 Abortion	65		
14 Immediate family member sent to jail	61		
15 New problem related to use of drugs or alcohol	59		
16 Immediate family member seriously ill	59		
17 Sex difficulties	57		
18 Death of a close friend	55		

EVENT	ADJUSTMENT SCORE	DID HAPPEN	HIGH IMPACT
19 Sudden increase in number of arguments with partner	55		
20 Period of homelessness	51		
21 Break-up with partner	51		
22 Marriage	50		
23 Serious restriction of social life	49		
24 Own/partner's pregnancy	49		
25 Problem with children	49		
26 Onset of prolonged ill health requiring treatment by a doctor	48		
27 New job in a new line of work	46		
28 Son or daughter left home	44		
29 Sudden increase in the number of family arguments	43		
30 Addition of new immediate family member	43		
31 Purchasing a home; taking a mortgage	40		
32 Moving to a new house	40		
33 Involvement in a physical fight	38		
34 Partner begins or stops work	34		
35 Minor violation of the law	34		
36 New job in the same line of work	31		
37 Change in hours or conditions in present job	31		

EVENT	ADJUSTMENT SCORE	DID HAPPEN	HIGH IMPACT
38 Going away for holiday	27		
39 Quarrel with neighbours	26		
40 Developing friendship with new neighbours	18		
		TOTAL SCORE	HIGH IMPACT SCORE

Above items adapted from R Cochrane and A Robertson. 'The Life events inventory' *Journal of psychosomatic research*, 1967, 11, 213–218. Used with permission.

When you have completed these two questionnaires, enter your scores on the following scale. For example, if you scored 262, your completed scale would look like this:

```
                               (262)
94        151       192     243 |  280       327       373       430       503
                                 ┴
Low risk                    Moderate risk                    High risk
```

The higher the scores, the higher the risk to your health, especially if your score falls in the High risk areas of the scale.

Changes in employment situation total

```
     94    151    192    243    280    327    373    430    503
     /      /      /      /      /      /      /      /      /
    10     20     30     40     50     60     70     80     90
  Low risk              Moderate risk                    High risk
```

High Impact

```
     0      0     32     60     87    116    160    219    292
     /      /      /      /      /      /      /      /      /
    10     20     30     40     50     60     70     80     90
  Low risk              Moderate risk                    High risk
```

Changes in situation away from employment total

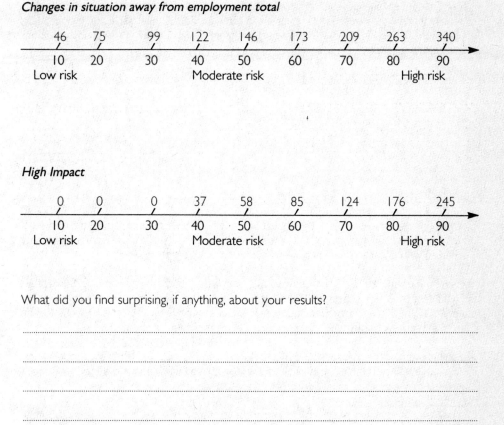

High Impact

What did you find surprising, if anything, about your results?

....

....

....

....

....

Impact of Change

Changes are likely to be stressful because they usually require people to make adjustments. The change events mentioned in this section have been monitored so that we can calculate the *average* amount of readjustment needed for each event. Many studies have shown that when we are adjusting to changes our health and performance suffer; the more changes, the more stress we experience.

However, not everyone experiences change events as having the average amount of impact. Those events that have the highest impact or surprise are more likely to increase the risk of adverse health changes than those which have little impact on us. This is the reason why the first questionnaire sections asked you to indicate which events actually happened to you, and then you were asked to assess whether events had a high or low impact on you.

If your total scores were in the High Risk areas, you should try to adjust to recent changes – especially those which were high impact – and avoid further changes for a few months. Can you think of any ways in which you can adjust to change more quickly? Write your suggestions in the following space.

....

....

....

....

....

One way in which you can lower the impact of change is to take steps to reduce the degree of *novelty* involved. By reducing the surprise impact and the unfamiliarity and uncertainty associated with change you can also lower your stress reactions.

Surprise can often be avoided or reduced by improved anticipation and planning. Sometimes you can negotiate with others in order to get advanced warnings of necessary changes. For example, if you have a regular assessment session at work you could also use that as an opportunity to ask about the future plans of the department or company.

As well as planning for change, it is helpful to discard some questionable beliefs about change; for example, 'Once this change is in place, I will be able to enjoy a stable period.' It is more than likely that we will all experience continuing changes throughout our lives.

Unfamiliarity and uncertainty can often be reduced by actively seeking *information* about the new situation; by developing the *skills* that will be needed to handle the new situation, and by developing a more positive, confident, opportunity-oriented set of *attitudes* about the new situation. Try to think of change as presenting a challenge, like the Chinese symbol for change which can mean danger or opportunity.

危机

As you review the biggest work and away from work changes you have experienced in the past year, what additional information do you need to get to finish incorporating the changes? What skills do you need to develop or acquire in order to handle the new situation better? And what might you do about your attitudes towards these changes? Write your feelings and ideas in the following box.

Another way you can reduce the overall impact of episodic stressors is to avoid further changes in your life – to the extent that this is possible! – while completing present changes. For example, if you are getting married and moving to a new city, it might be wise to delay a planned new career for a while, as you adapt to these other changes.

Chronic Stressful Conditions At Work

This section describes many of the chronic or daily situations which have been found to cause stress reactions in people during the course of their work. Please note how often you are experiencing each of these conditions by placing the appropriate numbers on the lines beside the conditions. Then total up your score and go on to the next questionnaire.

0 = Never   3 = Sometimes
1 = Very Rarely 4 = Often
2 = Rarely   5 = Always

1   I am unclear about what is expected of me.

2   Others I work with seem unclear about what my job is.

3   I have differences of opinion with my superiors.

4   Demands for my time at work are in conflict with each other.

5   I lack confidence in 'management'.

6   'Management' expects me to interrupt my work for new priorities.

7 There is conflict between my unit and other units.

8 I only get feedback when my performance is unsatisfactory.

9 Decisions or changes which affect me are made above without my knowledge or involvement.

10 I have to accept others' decisions without being told why.

11 I must attend meetings to get my job done.

12 I am cautious about what I say in meetings.

13 I have too much to do and too little time to do it.

14 I do not have enough work to do.

15 I feel over-qualified for the work I actually do.

16 I feel under-qualified for the work I actually do.

17 The people I work with closely are trained in a different field from me.

18 I must go to other departments to get my job done.

19 I have unsettled conflicts with the people I work with.

20 I get no personal support from the people I work with.

21 I spend my time 'fighting fires' rather than working to a plan.

22 I work in a situation where I am the only one of my sex, race, or age group.

23 I do not have the right amount of interaction (too much or too little) at work.

24 I do not have the right amount of supervision (too much or too little) at work.

25 I do not have the opportunity to use my knowledge and skills on the job.

26 I do not receive meaningful work assignments.

TOTAL SCORE

Chronic Stressful Conditions Away From Work

This section contains many of the chronic or daily situations which stimulate stress reactions in people in their lives away from work. Again, note how often you are experiencing each of these conditions by placing the appropriate numbers on the lines beside the conditions. Total up your score, and then add both totals to the scales below.

0 = Never
1 = Very Rarely
2 = Rarely
3 = Sometimes
4 = Often
5 = Always

1	Noise (traffic, aircraft, neighbours, etc.)	
2	Environmental pollution	
3	Concern about standard of living and ability to make ends meet financially	
4	Crime and vandalism in my immediate neighbourhood	
5	Law and order in society	
6	Personal long-term ill health	
7	Long-term ill health of a family member or close friend	
8	Racial tensions/racism	
9	Regular drug or alcohol abuse by a family member or close friend	
10	Concern over future of own career	
11	Concern over values/behaviour of family members	
12	Political situation in this country	
13	Possibility of war	
14	Financing own retirement, children's education, etc.	

15 Economic situation in this country	
16 Changing morals in our society (about family life, sexuality, etc.)	
17 Sexism	
18 Unresolved role/identity conflicts; mother-manager, president-retiree, etc.	
19 Chronic worry or guilt	
TOTAL SCORE	

Chronic stressful conditions in employment situation

12	22	26	29	33	36	43	47	50
10	20	30	40	50	60	70	80	90
Low risk			Moderate risk				High risk	

Chronic stressful conditions away from employment situation

10	12	16	20	25	28	34	39	44
10	20	30	40	50	60	70	80	90
Low risk			Moderate risk				High risk	

Some people experience the chronic, everyday pressures and tensions mentioned in the questionnaires as being even more stressful than the episodic changes discussed in the previous section. Such conditions are present every day and can cause a constant state of tension. The more stressful the conditions are, the more likely it is that health, morale and work effectiveness will suffer.

Not everyone experiences the same level of stress when confronted with these conditions. However, there is plenty of evidence to suggest that prolonged exposure to chronic stress conditions will eventually have a negative effect. If you scored in the Moderate to High risk areas it is time to do something about your stress levels! Can you think of any ways in which you can do this?

If you wish to lower your chronic stress scores, you have four alternatives to choose from.

Firstly, you may decide to *leave the situation*. This may involve something as minor as requesting a change of work assignment, or it could be something as major as a complete career change. It could mean redefining your relationships or even leaving them. You could also leave the situation temporarily by taking more short breaks, which will enable you to catch your breath and re-evaluate your situation.

Secondly, you could choose to stay in the stressful situation but *accept it as it is*. This may not change anything outwardly, but if you *choose* not to worry about irrelevant or unchangeable things they will not have as much impact on you. It has been estimated that 40% of the things we worry about never actually happen; 30% of the things we worry about are beyond our control and 20% of the things we worry about are trivial matters. That means that only 10% of our problems are really worth worrying about!

The third way in which you can lower your stress score is to do something to *change yourself*. This may mean developing a more constructive attitude, acquiring more information, or developing skills to change the situation. In reviewing the primary chronic sources of stress in your life today, what attitude, information and skill changes would help you most? Write your answers in the space below.

....

....

....

....

The fourth option is to *change the stressful condition* itself. This option is likely to mean changing your relationships with a partner, relative, colleague or supervisor. If you decide to change the stressful condition you must be prepared for some resistance to your proposed changes. Follow these guidelines to help you cope with this resistance.

- Establish or increase the belief that the change you wish to bring about is possible and desirable. People are usually reluctant to give up established habits and routines unless they feel that a change would have positive benefits.

- Increase the level, or establish awareness, of dissatisfaction. A positive way to accomplish this is to describe a vision of how the situation could be, and how everyone could benefit from it.

- Establish clear goals for yourself, your colleagues and friends which are understood and accepted. A good definition of 'depression' is 'dissatisfaction without any goals for improvement'.

- Identify first steps. A lot of good plans for change never get off the ground, because no one knows what to do first! In most cases, a small but successful first step in the right direction is all that is needed to set you on the road to change.

- Consider how other people can ensure your success. Is there someone who can make a habit change with you, or who will challenge and encourage you to maintain a change? For example, could your partner help you find a more rewarding job? Also think about the kinds of expert advice, access to information or direct help you will need to be successful. Identify key people and ask them to help you make the change.

When you follow these five steps, resistance will disappear and change will become possible. Make a note of stressful situations that you would like to change.

....

....

....

....

Select a few of the chronic stress situations which you find stressful and would like to change and apply these five steps. You will be pleasantly surprised at how much easier change becomes.

Section Three: Reactions and Ways of Coping

Our natural physical and psychological responses to excessive pressure are called *strain*. The following are among the most common strain responses. Please note how often you have experienced each of these responses over the past few weeks, by placing the appropriate numbers on the lines beside the responses.

0 = Never
1 = Very Rarely
2 = Rarely
3 = Sometimes
4 = Often
5 = Always

1 Eat too much	
2 Drink too much alcohol	
3 Smoke more than usual	
4 Feel tense, uptight, fidgety, nervous	
5 Feel depressed or remorseful	
6 Like myself less	
7 Have difficulty going to sleep or staying asleep	
8 Feel restless and unable to concentrate	
9 Have decreased interest in sex	
10 Have increased interest in sex	
11 Loss of appetite	
12 Feel tired, low energy, excessive fatigue	
13 Feel irritable	

14	Think about suicide	
15	Become less communicative	
16	Feel disoriented or overwhelmed	
17	Difficulty getting up in the morning	
18	Headaches	
19	Upset stomach or intestinal problems	
20	Sweaty and/or trembling hands	
21	Shortness of breath and sighing	
22	Let things slide	
23	Misdirected anger	
24	Feel unhealthy	
25	Feel weak	
26	Feel dizzy or lightheaded	
	TOTAL SCORE	

The strain response

13	17		22		27		32		36		41		49		58

10	20	30	40	50	60	70	80	90
Low risk			Moderate risk				High risk	

Strain is evidence that the level of stress one is experiencing is taking its toll – it is the result of accumulated and unexpressed 'fight or flight'. If you have a high strain score for an extended period of time, it becomes increasingly likely that you will experience adverse health changes.

It is important that you become aware of which specific strain responses serve as your early warning signals. If you can learn to read and respond appropriately to these signals, you can protect yourself from the adverse effects of too much stress.

Your early warning signals are probably included in the Strain Response questionnaire; look at the responses where you scored 4 or 5. What are your particular responses to stress?

....

....

....

Another way of exploring the strain response is to consider it to be a measure of the status of your health 'account'. A score above the half-way mark suggests that you are making withdrawals from your account. You won't ever know what the balance is in your health account, but you can be sure that overdrafts bring a high service charge with them! Scores in the Low risk area of the scale suggest that you are making deposits into your account. You still don't know the balance in the account, but you do know that it is increasing!

There are three excellent and straightforward ways to directly reduce your strain level.

Regular physical exercise such as walking, jogging, bicycling, or swimming are all forms of 'flight' and, as such, burn up or metabolise the stress hormones which have been released into your blood stream and are operating to maintain a fight or flight readiness.

Regular periods of relaxation such as meditation, prayer, or just sitting in the garden actually cause that part of your central nervous system, the hypothalamus, which is originating the fight or flight messages, to send out different more relaxing messages to your body.

Good nutritional practices can help by providing plenty of the B and C vitamins, which are burned up very rapidly when you are under stress. Most of these are located in fruits, vegetables, and grains, which are often omitted in favour of convenience and junk foods during periods of stress. What's more, alcohol, caffeine, sugar and tobacco, which are all antagonistic to the B and C vitamins, are often consumed in greater quantities during stressful periods. Each of the nutrients in B and C vitamins serve many functions in our bodies and minds, and if they are being burned up more quickly than usual, or we aren't consuming enough of them, or they are less efficient because of high 'junk' intake, then its little wonder that our mental functioning and physical performance suffer when we are under stress.

Psychological Outlook

There is mounting evidence that the self-fulfilling prophecy is a very major factor in determining one's health. People with positive, optimistic outlooks, who feel they are in charge of their lives and who expect to be healthy, generally remain healthy even after period of intense stress. On the other hand, people with negative, pessimistic outlooks, who feel they have no control over their lives and expect to become ill, generally experience more illness even if stress levels remain moderate. In a nutshell, we become what we think about – what we expect to happen tends to happen.

To assess your own psychological outlook respond to the following items by placing the appropriate numbers beside the items.

1 = Poor, Extremely unhappy, Extremely likely, Rarely or Never, Not at all, None
2 = Poor to average
3 = Average
4 = Above average
5 = Excellent, Extremely satisfied, Extremely unlikely, Always, Completely, A great deal

1	In relation to other people, how would you rate your present health?	
2	In general, how satisfied are you with your lifestyle at present?	
3	If you make no changes in your present lifestyle, how likely do you think it is that you will develop a serious illness in the next five years?	
4	How often do you feel a sense of fulfilment and accomplishment at the end of the day?	
5	To what extent do you feel responsible for your present situation and level of well-being?	
6	How regularly do you strive to become more knowledgeable about yourself?	
7	How adequately are you supported by your spiritual or religious beliefs?	

8	To what extent is your life full of interesting and exciting things?	
9	How frequently do you feel optimistic and confident in your abilities?	
10	To what extent do you treat others with care, sensitivity and respect?	
11	How much value do you place on your feelings?	
12	How readily do you acknowledge and share your feelings with others?	
13	How much of the time do you feel that you are in control of your life and what happens to you?	
14	How much importance do you attach to your present work?	
15	To what extent does life present you with interesting challenges?	
	TOTAL SCORE	

Psychological Outlook

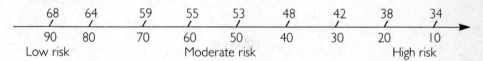

68	64	59	55	53	48	42	38	34
90	80	70	60	50	40	30	20	10
Low risk			Moderate risk				High risk	

The kinds of things which most of us need to do in order to manage our stress levels more effectively and to improve our health reserves are relatively straightforward, and yet many people seem unable to carry through their improvement intentions. The new exercise programme lasts only a few weeks; the lost weight is regained; and the time management practices are gradually forgotten or declared to be unrealistic. This section is intended to explore why this happens so frequently.

Our *perceptions* determine what we actually *experience* in a situation, by making us receptive to some stimuli and blind to other stimuli. People who expect to find problems in a given situation are usually able to find them, while others who expect to find opportunities in the same situation will actually be successful.

31

The *experiences* we have determine our *outlook*. Beliefs and attitudes are formed as a result of the repetitive thematic messages we get from outside authorities, as well as those we give ourselves by means of our inner self-talk. If we repeatedly learn that we are 'not ready yet' from our parents and teachers, we are likely to develop a cautious, 'wait and see' outlook on life.

Our *outlook* determines what we perceive in a situation. A person who has an optimistic, positive, self-directed outlook will generally expect to find opportunities; while another person who has a pessimistic, negative, disempowered outlook will generally expect to find difficulties.

And, as the diagram below indicates, we have come full circle.

Perceptions
determine
experiences

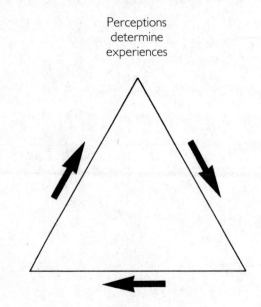

Experiences
determines
outlook

Outlook
determines
perceptions

In this matter, our general outlook becomes self-fulfilling and self-reinforcing. In order to be fully successful in implementing our plans for improved stress management and health, it is likely that each of us will have to break into this cycle to create new beliefs and expectations which support the changes we wish to make.

How would you characterise your own general outlook?

For each negative thought pattern that you identify, create a reverse image of the pattern, and practise holding this positive new image in your mind *as if it were already true*, for the next few days. The more repetitions you can create of dwelling on this desired new image, the more quickly it will become a permanent part of your revised general outlook! Repeat this exercise for each item on the General Outlook questionnaire on which you scored three or less. You will be amazed at how much your overall outlook can be changed when you take control of it.

General Lifestyle

This section contains an overview of some of the basic lifestyle areas which have been found to have an important bearing on withstanding excessive stress *and* on protecting and promoting health. You are asked to make two responses to each item:

- How important do you personally feel the item is?

- How well do you think you are doing in each area at present?

1 = Not important, Very poorly
2 = Of slight importance, not very well
3 = Somewhat important, quite well
4 = Important, good
5 = Very important, excellent

Importance to Health	Present Effectiveness	
		1 Moderate, optimistic outlook
		2 High quality relationships
		3 Balanced diet
		4 Vitamin/mineral supplements
		5 Maintain recommended weight
		6 Average two or less alcoholic drinks per day
		7 Not using tobacco
		8 Regular physical check-ups
		9 Vigorous regular exercise
		10 Moderating impatience
		11 Regular relaxation practice
		12 Seat belt use and defensive driving
		TOTAL

General life style – Importance

60	60		58	56	54	52	51	47	42
90	80		70	60	50	40	30	20	10
Low risk				Moderate risk				High risk	

General life style – Present effectiveness

54	51		49	46	43	39	36	33	29
90	80		70	60	50	40	30	20	10
Low risk				Moderate risk				High risk	

This General Lifestyle section of the workbook provides an overview of the rest of the workbook – it gives you a quick snapshot of the lifestyle areas where you are doing well and indicates those which need improvements. Recall that approximately 54% of the risks to your health are lifestyle factors. Most of these are contained in the dozen items in this questionnaire section.

Each of the 12 lifestyle habits in the section are very important to your day to day health and performance as well as playing a significant part in how long you can expect to live. Any of these items which need improvement can be improved should you decide to do so. After reviewing your results on this section of the questionnaire, what are your priorities for improvement?

....

....

....

....

....

....

....

Social Support

The network of family, friends, colleagues and advisers to which you can turn can be a very important factor in handling stress and in maintaining your good health. Read the following list and indicate how you feel about each source of support by placing the appropriate number next to each item.

1 = Highly dissatisfied
2 = Dissatisfied
3 = Medium satisfaction or not applicable
4 = Satisfied
5 = Highly satisfied

1 Immediate family members	
2 Relatives	
3 In-laws	
4 Friends	
5 Experts (doctors, plumbers, lawyers, teachers, etc.)	
6 Helpers (people who are happy to provide direct help)	
7 Reference groups (race, gender, professional club, etc.)	
8 Challengers (people who encourage you to excel and grow)	
9 Access providers (people who can link you to people or things you need or want)	
10 Energisers (people who excite or stimulate you)	
11 Respecters (people who make you feel good about yourself)	
TOTAL	

Social support

49	45		41	39	37	35	32	29	24
90	80		70	60	50	40	30	20	10
Low risk				Moderate risk				High risk	

Social support is an important health promotion factor as well as a very important part of stress management. People with plenty of social support in their lives generally experience better health than those who have inadequate social support.

35

What's more, one of the best ways to get through a stressful period is to turn to a social support network for counselling, encouragement, direct assistance or expertise. Unfortunately, many people have a tendency to withdraw from their support networks during times of stress, rather than actively use them for support.

Frequently, it also happens that one or more key members of your social support network engage in the same high risk lifestyle choices, (for example, smoking) which you may wish to change. As a result, they may not be very supportive of the changes you wish to make and may even actively oppose you! Thus you may find it necessary to do some specific negotiating or bargaining. For example, you and your colleagues might agree not to smoke in the office. As your outlook and habits change you may even find it necessary to change or perhaps end some relationships, and form new more supportive relationships.

In reviewing your responses to the Social Support questionnaire section, try to answer the following questions:

How do you feel about the size of your present social support network?

....

How do you feel about the diversity of your present social support network?

....

Are you relying on a very few people for too many different social support qualities?

....

Do any of your present relationships with people in your social support network need improvement? In what ways?

....

....

....

Are any of your present relationships with people in your social support network beyond saving – needing to be ended? Why is this?

....

....

....

Are there any important social support qualities (e.g. expertise, challenge, etc.) missing from your present social support network? What are they?

....

....

Do you know people who would be valuable additions to your social support network?

....

....

Are the members of your present social support network aware that you consider them to be your supporters?

....

As you reflect on your present social support network and any needs for change, what is the one step that you can take in the near future to improve the quality of your social support?

....

....

....

Section Four: Diet and Exercise

Nutrition has emerged as a central factor in maintaining and improving health, especially during periods of high stress. To check your current attitudes to nutrition and diet, describe your present eating habits and nutritional awareness by placing the appropriate numbers beside the following items.

0 = Never
1 = Very rarely
2 = Rarely
3 = Sometimes
4 = Often
5 = Always

1 Cooking and meal times are a source of happiness	
2 Take time for leisurely meals	
3 Set aside worries, anger and troubles during meal times	
4 Read and educate yourself about good nutrition	
5 Know your own nutritional needs and how to meet them	
6 Eat a well-balanced breakfast	
7 Eat three or more well-balanced meals per day	
8 Eat fruits and vegetables every day	
9 Eat whole grains every day	
10 Regularly include enough fibre in your diet	
11 Keep your weight within ten pounds of what you would ideally like	
12 Awareness of the effect of blood sugar levels on energy level and performance	
13 Awareness of the effects of food allergies or sensitivities on your energy level and performance	

14 Chew your food thoroughly	
15 Informed about your needs for nutritional supplements	
16 Openness to changing your eating habits as you gain new information	
Subtotal A (Items 1–16)	
17 Use processed foods and packaged meals	
18 Eating habits change when you are upset or bored	
19 Add sugar (white, brown or honey) to your food	
20 Average more than two alcoholic drinks per day	
21 Average more than three caffeinated drinks per day	
22 Use tobacco	
Subtotal B (Items 17–22)	
Total score is subtotal A minus subtotal B	

Nutritional habits and awareness

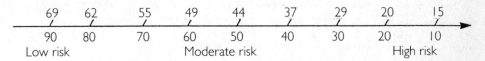

Sound nutritional practices are essential for long-term positive health and stress management. If you eat well, you will be supplying your body with all the nutrients it needs (many are needed in higher quantities during stressful periods) and your resistance to illness will be increased. What do you think makes for a healthy, balanced diet? Write some ideas in the box below.

A good eating plan should include a variety of foods, including cereals, grains, fruits, vegetables, dairy products and protein. It should minimise refined white flour, sugar, salt, saturated fats, artificial additives and alcohol. It also means getting the right balance of vitamins and minerals. The chart on the following two pages gives details of the various vitamins we need, and how they can be obtained.

Minerals

A lot of attention has recently been focused on the role of minerals in keeping us healthy. Although they are readily available in most diets, they are used up very rapidly in times of stress. Fresh vegetables and fruits are the best source of many minerals, as long as they are not over-cooked or soaked for too long. Meat provides a good source of iron, as do green vegetables. Calcium is readily available from dairy products – remember when school children used to drink their daily bottle of milk? Refined foods, like bleached flour, often have reduced mineral content, so try to eat whole foods and fresh produce.

Zinc	Essential for mental alertness and speedy wound healing. Lack of this mineral can cause lack of appetite, brittle nails and loss of taste and smell.
Calcium	This is needed for healthy teeth and bones, and to maintain muscles and nerves. Vitamin D is needed to help absorb calcium.
Iron	Necessary for healthy blood, as it is needed to form the red blood cells which transport oxygen round the body. Deficiency is shown by constant tiredness and itchy skin.
Magnesium	Prolonged illness and heavy drinking can cut magnesium levels, so make sure you get enough of this mineral in stressful times. It helps fight depression, and can also help relieve stomach upsets.

You should also note that many vitamins and minerals cannot work alone; they need to work in combination to be effective. Thus it is even more important to make sure you eat a *balanced* diet. Too much of one vitamin or mineral, salt for instance, can be as harmful as too little.

The tendency in all affluent countries like Britain and the USA is to consume large amounts of animal protein and fats in the form of meats and cheeses. This is combined with a tendency to consume fewer complex carbohydrates like whole grains, nuts, fruits and vegetables. In addition, in a busy society, commercially prepared meals and convenience foods have taken precedence over whole, unprocessed foods, as we often assume that it takes too much time to prepare good meals.

VITAMIN	BEST FOOD SOURCES	FUNCTION	DEFICIENCY SIGNS	MINIMUM DAILY NEED	LACK MAY BE CAUSED BY:
A retinol	Fish liver oil, oily fish, liver, kidney, dairy foods, margarine, green vegetables, yellow fruit, carrots.	Essential for growth, health of eyes, structure and health of skin.	Low resistance to infection, night blindness, catarrhal and bronchial infections, skin complaints.	Children under 13: 1200iu (~ 360mcg) Adults: 2500iu (~ 750mcg).	Frying, canning, long term treatment with liquid paraffin, some drugs.
B1 thiamin	Yeast, wheat germ, meat, nuts, beans, whole grain foods, pulses, seafood.	Essential for growth, conversion of carbohydrates into energy, health of nerves, muscles.	Nervous disorders, easy exhaustion, depression, poor digestion.	Children under 13: 0.5mg Adults: 1mg.	Alcohol, tobacco smoke, over-cooking, sulphur dioxide, high sugar diets.
B2 riboflavin	Yeast, wheat germ, meat, soya beans, eggs, vegetables, milk, cheese.	Essential for growth, health of skin, mouth, eyes, general well-being.	Dry hair and skin, mouth sores, nervousness, lack of stamina.	Children under 13: 0.8mg. Adults: 17mg.	Contraceptive pill.
Pantothenic acid	Yeast, liver, wholemeal bread, brown rice, eggs, nuts.	Health of skin and hair, including hair growth. Needed for all tissue growth.	Dry skin and hair.	Children under 13: 2.5mg. Adults: 5-10mg.	Heating above boiling; absent from many refined foods.
B6 pyridoxine	Yeast, wheat germ, meat, fish, wholemeal products, milk, cabbage, oats.	Essential for body's use of protein, health of skin, nerves and muscle.	Irritability, depression, skin eruptions, insomnia, muscle cramps.	1mg. Women taking oral contraceptives need much more.	Loss in cooking and freezing, contraceptive pill, alcohol, smoking.
B12 cyanocobalamin	Liver and meat, eggs.	Health of nerves, blood and skin, body's use of protein, growth.	Anaemia, tiredness, skin disorders.	Children under 13: 0.5-1mcg disorders. Adults: 15mcg.	Veganism, malabsorption, contraceptive pill, many drugs, smoking.
Biotin (B group)	Liver, kidney, wheat germ, bran, oats, eggs, nuts.	Probably essential for healthy skin, nerves and muscles.	Falling hair, eczema.	Children under 13: 0.25mcg. Adults: 1mcg.	

VITAMIN	BEST FOOD SOURCES	FUNCTION	DEFICIENCY SIGNS	MINIMUM DAILY NEED	LACK MAY BE CAUSED BY:
Choline and inositol (B group)	Eggs, liver, yeast, offal, wheat germ, oats, nuts.	Both essential for functioning of liver, prevent build-up of fats in body.	Liver disorders, reduced alcohol tolerance.	Children under 13: 2.5mg. Adults: 10mg of each.	Deficiency unlikely.
Folic acid (B group)	Offal meats, green vegetables, yeast, wheat germ, soya flour.	Essential for all growth, healthy blood, fertility.	Anaemia, weakness, depression, diarrhoea.	0.5mg.	Pregnancy, many drugs including contraceptive pill, prolonged cooking.
Niacin nicotinic acid (B group)	Meat, fish, whole grain products, peanuts.	Essential for growth, health of skin, digestion of carbohydrates, nervous system.	Skin disorders, nervous and intestinal upset, headaches, insomnia.	Children under 13: 5-10mg. Adults: 15-18mg.	Missing from over-refined foods.
C ascorbic acid	Citrus fruit, other fruit, raw vegetables, green and red peppers, potatoes.	Essential to health of cells, blood vessels, gums and teeth, healing of wounds.	Sore gums, low resistance to infection, slow healing, painful joints.	30mg is minimum.	Many drugs including aspirin, corticosteroids, contraceptive pill, over-cooking, refining of foods, alcohol, smoking.
D calciferol	Fish liver oils, sunshine on skin, oily fish, butter and margarine, eggs.	Formation of bones and teeth, needed for calcium and phosphorus use.	Retarded growth, crooked bones (rickets), tooth decay, weak muscles.	Children under 13: 400iu Adults: 100iu.	Lack of sunshine or dairy foods; other factors as vitamin A.
E tocopherol	Vegetable oils, wheat germ, wholemeal bread, egg yolks, green vegetables, nuts.	Known to be essential, but function not fully understood. Needed for fertility and muscle health by animals.	Lack causes muscular disorders, infertility and nervous disorders in animals.	Not certain, but estimated at 10mg.	Air, light, deep freezing, frying, losses in refining of vegetable oils, contraceptive pill
K	Green vegetables, soya beans, liver, oils.	Essential for blood clotting.	Prolonged bleeding from cuts or sores.	Unknown.	Similar to E: antibiotics, liquid paraffin, malabsorption, diseases.

Jot down which eating problems (i.e. too much or too little of certain foods) are predominant in our society:

For most people, the major problems connected with eating habits are as follows:

Excessive Fat

Most people eat far too much fat – on average about 45% of our calories. Nutritionists suggest that we should consume only 25% of our calories in the form of fats. Excessive fat consumption is implicated as a risk factor for cardiovascular diseases and several forms of cancer. Can you think of any way in which you could reduce your intake of fats?

....

....

....

We suggest that you can control your intake of saturated fats by eating less red meat, high fat cheeses, dairy produce, palm and coconut oils. Reduce the amount of fried foods you eat, together with cakes, pastries and chocolate.

Instead, eat chicken, fish or vegetables cooked with little or no fat. Skimmed or semi-skimmed milk is a good idea, as it still contains calcium, but has a reduced fat content. Also look out for reduced fat cheeses, yoghurts, etc. If you use oils and spreads, try to use the ones marked 'high in polyunsaturates'.

Instead of eating cakes and sweets at the end of a meal, eat fruit instead. There are many exotic varieties of fruit now available, so your choice need not be limited to apples and oranges! By cutting down like this you will not only do your heart good – you will probably lose weight too, especially if you also follow the next set of guidelines.

Excessive Sugar

The annual per capita consumption of sugar is increasing, and now exceeds 125 pounds per year. Some of this sugar occurs naturally in foods, but about two-thirds of this sugar is added by food manufacturers. For example, a 12oz can of soft drink contains between nine and eleven teaspoons of sugar. In addition to adding many unnecessary calories to the diet, sugar uses up a great many B and C vitamins and causes triglycerides, a cardiovascular risk factor, to increase. Most people who consume sugary foods eat something containing sugar every two to three hours to maintain their energy.

You can cut down on your sugar intake by avoiding sweets, cakes and soft drinks. Many processed foods contain large amounts of sugar, so steer clear of these or read the ingredients carefully to check sugar levels.

Excessive Salt

We need small amounts of sodium on a daily basis, but most people eat five to ten times more than they need. This causes fluid retention on the cellular level, forcing the heart to work harder to feed the cells. As a result, blood pressure elevates.

Try reducing salt levels in your food, or use a salt substitute. There are hundreds of herbs and spices which can add flavour to food but don't have the harmful effects of too much salt.

Insufficient Fibre

Most people get only about 15% of their calories from fruits, vegetables, grains, cereals and nuts – plant foods. Nutritionists tell us we should be getting four times that much! All of the fibre in our diet must come from plant sources.

Fibre is necessary for gastrointestinal health (it probably prevents colon cancer), and can significantly reduce cholesterol. There are many kinds of fibre necessary, and you can only get the full range by eating a broad range of plant food. They are also the main sources of vitamins B and C, which are essential in greater quantities during times of stress. The action here is obvious – cut down on meats, cheeses, fatty and sugary food and eat more plant foods!

Excessive Caffeine

There are about 100mg of caffeine in a cup of coffee. People who have over 300mg of caffeine a day have increasingly irregular heart beats. It also stimulates the adrenal glands to produce stress hormones. Caffeine is also antagonistic to B and C vitamins and drops the blood sugar, stimulating feelings of hunger. Instead of drinking coffee, try to drink more fruit juices, teas or mineral waters.

Try keeping an eating diary for a week, logging in everything you eat or drink. Then, go over your entries and estimate your total calorie consumption.

Most people want to lose several pounds – if this is true for you, where in your diet can you cut fat and sugar calories? If you use the above five nutritional problems as a guide, analyse your food diary and note where the excesses and the deficiencies are. You should be able to note some clear patterns in your eating habits regarding fat, sugar, salt, caffeine and complex carbohydrate consumption. Necessary changes should be obvious, so write down some possible alterations to your diet.

....

....

....

One of the most important things to consider relative to stress and health is the need for B and C vitamins. These are burned up very quickly under stress and are in somewhat short supply in most diets. A further complication is that sugar, caffeine, tobacco and alcohol all diminish the availability of these necessary nutrients. If you consume a lot of any of these substances during periods of stress, you are adding to your problem. Be sure to eat plenty of fibre and complex carbohydrates, and avoid sugar, caffeine, tobacco and alcohol if your strain score is elevated.

Physical Exercise Habits And Awareness

Regular physical exercise is an excellent way to alleviate stress and to improve circulation, metabolism, flexibility and heart and lung efficiency. It can also enhance mood and creativity and alleviate pain. Please indicate your present exercise habits by placing the appropriate numbers on the lines beside the items.

0 = Never, Not at all
1 = Rarely
2 = Infrequently
3 = Sometimes, good intentions!
4 = Often, usually
5 = Always, regularly

1	Take some form of recreational exercise (slow walking, golf, bowling, gardening, etc.) at least weekly	
2	Take some form of stretching exercise at least three times a week	
3	Jog two miles in 18 minutes or walk three miles in 42 minutes (or the equivalent) three to five times per week	
4	Find exercise to be an enjoyable and rewarding pastime	
5	Aware of the effects of your present exercise level on your resting pulse rate	
6	Aware of the effects of your present exercise level on your blood pressure	
7	Aware of the effects of your present exercise level on your digestion and metabolism	

8	Aware of the effects of your present exercise level on your energy level and performance	
9	Aware of the effects of your present exercise level on your body-fat percentage	
10	Aware of the effects of your present exercise level on your general mood and level of self-confidence	
	TOTAL	

Physical exercise habits and awareness

47	42	38	35	32	28	23	19	13
90	80	70	60	50	40	30	20	10
Low risk			Moderate risk				High risk	

Our bodies are designed to be used vigorously and we have become sedentary. It has been estimated that in the middle of the 19th century at least one third of the power used in work was supplied by human muscle; and that today that figure is less than one half of one per cent. Without sufficient exercise, we can tolerate fewer calories and are less sharp mentally and less co-ordinated physically. Our cardiovascular and respiratory systems become sluggish and we break down faster.

Stress causes the endocrine glands to produce 'fight or flight' hormones which, if not expressed, accumulate and drive our strain scores up. Regular vigorous exercise (20–30 minutes per session, three to five sessions per week of sustained exertion) burns up these 'fight or flight' hormones and helps your body chemistry return to normal. What are some of the benefits of physical exercise?

....

....

....

....

Exercising at the levels mentioned above has benefits which help to restore or protect health. In many cases vigorous regular exercise causes a lowering of blood pressure. It also lowers the resting pulse rate, indicating that the heart and lungs have become stronger. Exercise normalises metabolism and improves digestion, which are added aids to weight control. And furthermore, exercise can burn up excess body fat and improve both your energy level and your performance.

On the psychological level, exercise can improve mood, confidence and creativity by triggering the production of brain chemicals called *endorphins*. These endorphins also serve to alleviate pain and withdrawal symptoms, when generated by increased physical activity – making exercise an excellent support for people who are giving up alcohol or tobacco!

There are many good books published on exercise which may be of assistance to you. All of them suggest that you have a thorough physical check-up before beginning, and that you develop your level of fitness gradually. You should select an exercise programme (running, swimming, walking, bicycling, stationary machines) which you enjoy. It doesn't have to be a drudgery or boring – it should be stimulating and enjoyable. Try several things and find what suits you best!

What goal are you setting for yourself to improve your physical fitness?

....

....

....

Drinking Habits

Alcohol is an obvious risk factor to health when abused. The questions which follow have been demonstrated to be very useful in identifying when people have a problem with alcohol. For each of the following questions which is true about you, place an X in the Yes column on the line beside the question. For each question which is not true of you, place an X in the No column on the line beside the question.

	YES	NO
1 Do you feel that you are a normal drinker? (Yes, if you do not use alcohol at present.)		
2 Have you ever woken up in the morning after drinking the night before and found that you could not remember a part of the evening?		
3 Does your partner or family ever worry or complain about your drinking?		
4 Can you stop drinking without a struggle after one or two drinks?		

	YES	NO
5 Do you ever feel bad about your drinking?		
6 Do your friends and relatives think you are a normal drinker?		
7 Do you ever try to limit your drinking to certain times of day or certain places?		
8 Are you ALWAYS able to stop drinking when you want to?		
9 Have you ever attended a meeting of Alcoholics Anonymous (AA)?		
10 Have you got into fights when drinking?		
11 Has drinking ever created problems between you and your partner or family?		
12 Has your partner, or another family member, ever gone to anyone for help about your drinking?		
13 Have you ever lost friends because of your drinking?		
14 Have you ever got into trouble at work because of your drinking?		
15 Have you ever lost a job because of your drinking?		
16 Have you ever neglected your obligations, your family, or your work for two or more days in a row because you were drinking?		
17 Do you drink before noon fairly often?		
18 Have you ever been told that you have liver trouble? Cirrhosis?		
19 Have you ever had delirium tremens (DTs), severe shaking, heard voices, or seen things that weren't there after heavy drinking?		
20 Have you ever gone to anyone for help about your drinking?		
21 Have you ever been in a hospital because of your drinking?		

	YES	NO
22 Have you ever been a patient in a psychiatric hospital or on a psychiatric ward of a general hospital where drinking was part of the problem?		
23 Have you ever been seen at a psychiatric or mental health clinic, or gone to a doctor, social worker, or clergyman for help with an emotional problem in which drinking played a part?		
24 Have you ever been arrested, even for a few hours, because of drunken behaviour?		
25 Have you ever been arrested for drunk driving or for driving after drinking?		

SCORING KEY

This questionnaire is scored by giving yourself one point for each 'key' response. Your total score is the number of 'key' responses. The 'key' responses are as follows:

1	NO	10	YES	18	YES		
2	YES	11	YES	19	YES		
3	YES	12	YES	20	YES		
4	NO	13	YES	21	YES		
5	YES	14	YES	22	YES		
6	NO	15	YES	23	YES		
7	YES	16	YES	24	YES		
8	NO	17	YES	25	YES		
9	YES						

_____ TOTAL SCORE*

Drinking habits score

0–3	=	No drinking problem
4–6	=	Potential alcohol problem
7–25	=	It would appear that you already have an alcohol problem. We suggest that you seek some professional help or advice as soon as possible.

*Reprinted with permission of the AAA Foundation for Traffic Safety from the *DWI Counselling Manual*.

For many people, one or two drinks a day may be relaxing and a means to enliven social interactions. When taken in larger amounts, alcohol has a depressant effect and directly affects behaviour, reflexes, self-control and judgement. Thus the risk of an accident is dramatically increased as more alcohol is consumed. Alcohol is the single biggest factor in all road deaths and injuries.

The risks of serious illnesses are also increased by continual heavy drinking – cirrhosis, cancer, pneumonia, and heart disease are all made more likely. The abuse of alcohol is also implicated in a high percentage of cases of family problems and financial and job difficulties.

It is estimated that between 8–14 million days are lost at work because of heavy drinking. At work, alcohol (and drug) abusers are three times as likely to be late, use three times as much sick leave, make five times as many compensation claims, and have more than three times as many accidents as non-users.

Can you think of any ways in which you can cut down your alcohol intake?

....

....

....

We suggest that you start by keeping a Drinking Diary to measure the average amount of alcohol you consume per week.

Also include the situation you were drinking in, e.g. at the pub with friends, lunchtime with family. You may find that there are times when you drink more than is necessary, perhaps after a hard day at work, or when you are with a particular friend. Make a note of these and watch for similar situations in the future.

If you scored in the risk area of the alcohol assessment questionnaire, you are encouraged to seek immediate assistance. Alcohol abuse is an extremely risky activity, and should not be treated lightly.

Section Five: Looking to the Future

Behavioural Habits

It is becoming clear that our behavioural patterns have a strong influence on health, as well as on what we find to be stressful and how we can best cope with excessive pressures. Please indicate how often each of the following behavioural habits is true of you by placing the appropriate number on the line beside the habit.

0 = Never
1 = Very Rarely
2 = Rarely
3 = Sometimes
4 = Often
5 = Always

	1	Schedule more and more activities into less and less time
	2	Become irritated and impatient when delayed or made to wait
	3	Become impatient when watching others do things you can do faster or better
	4	Have difficulty sitting and doing nothing
	5	Desire to win every game played, even when playing with children
	6	Work harder to get things done than most of your associates
	7	Become angry when you see inefficiency or carelessness in others

8	Become easily aggravated or frustrated over events which seem trivial a short while later
9	Keep yourself too busy to 'stop and smell the flowers'
10	Speak rapidly and hurry the speech of others
	TOTAL SCORE

Behavioural habits score

40–50 points	= Strong Type A	HIGH RISK
35–39 points	= Type A	MODERATE RISK
20–34 points	= Type AB	MODERATE RISK
15–19 points	= Type B	LOW RISK
0–14 points	= Strong Type B	LOW RISK

The Behavioural Habits questionnaire section measures Type A behaviour tendencies. Look at the following table for a brief outline of what are classed as Type A and Type B.

Type A	Type B
Competitive	Relaxed
Achiever	Easy-going
Fast worker	Seldom impatient
Aggressive	Takes time to enjoy pursuits outside the job
Impatient	Works steadily
Restless	Not easily irritated
Hyper-alert	Seldom short of time
Explosive speech	Moves and speaks slowly
Frequently feels under pressure	Not pre-occupied with achievement

Type As are also more likely to smoke, take little exercise and have fewer holidays than Type B – making their lifestyle even more stressful!

Which type are you? ....

Do you know someone who is the opposite? ....

Type A behaviour is now considered to be a primary risk factor for coronary heart disease. Those who regularly display excessive amounts of anger, impatience, irritability, and urgency, especially in situations in which these reactions can do nothing to resolve things, are much more likely to experience a heart attack than are those who permit themselves to take things as they come and who only 'engage' in situations that can be influenced. For example, losing one's temper in traffic jams or in queues at the bank does nothing to speed up traffic or the queue, but may do a great deal to speed up the onset of heart disease.

Type A behaviour causes your body to enter into and to maintain chronically the 'fight or flight' response. This means that total cholesterol, pulse rate, and blood pressure are likely to become chronically elevated. If your behavioural habits score is in the risk area, it may be important for you to learn that you can still work hard and not be irritable or aggressive at the same time. It is not the hard work or high productivity which is thought to be the risk factor.

One of the most important things for you to do if your score is in the risk area is to learn to relax. Relaxation reverses the signals the brain is sending out from 'fight or flight' to 'relaxation'. Many people who score high on measures of type A behaviour are very resistant to the idea of relaxation, stating that it is 'such a waste of time – you don't accomplish anything!' So, this suggestion of learning to relax is likely to stir up some resistance – especially if you really need to learn how! In reality, learning to relax effectively takes a great deal of discipline and determination – so approach it as a challenge.

Here are some methods of relaxation. See if you can add some more.

Going for a leisurely walk

LISTENING TO YOUR FAVOURITE MUSIC

Having a long, hot bath

Another suggested way to get control of type A impulses is to practise patience in situations which are out of your control and in which you often lose your temper and become impatient. The next time you find yourself in a traffic jam or at the end of a long queue at the bank, say to yourself 'I choose to remain calm' and see what happens. If you repeat this on each such occasion, you will soon find that you are not losing your temper nearly so often.

Additional Factors

This section contains various additional factors which have a bearing on health and stress management. You may not know your blood pressure and cholesterol levels, so omit these and make a note to ask your doctor next time you have a check-up.

1   Do you use tobacco? (YES or NO)

2   If you once smoked and have quit, how long has it been?
     (YEARS)

3   What is your blood pressure?

4   What is your cholesterol level?

Tobacco

Never smoked or quit over 15 years ago	Quit smoking 5–15 years ago	Quit less than 5 years ago	Current smoker less than 20 cigarettes a day	Current smoker 20–40 cigarettes a day	Current smoker more than 40 cigarettes a day
Low risk	Moderate risk		High risk		

Blood pressure

Systolic Reading	/	/	/	/	/	/	/
	UNDER 110	110	120	130	140	150	OVER 150
	Low risk					Moderate risk	High risk

Diastolic	/	/	/	/	/	/	/
	UNDER 70	70	80	90	100	110	OVER 110
	Low risk					Moderate risk	High risk

Total Cholesterol

Total Cholesterol	/	/	/	/	/	/
	170 & BELOW	190	210	230	250	270 & ABOVE
	Low risk		Moderate risk			High risk

Smoking

Smoking is the undisputed number one health risk in our lives today. A smoker is two or three times more likely to have a heart attack, and at least eight times more likely to develop lung cancer than a non-smoker. Smoking is the major cause of lung cancer, coronary heart disease and chronic obstructive lung diseases.

In order to stop smoking, an individual must first clearly choose to be a non-smoker. Once this fundamental choice is made, there are a number of methods available to support one in quitting.

A balanced diet and plenty of exercise are especially important during the period of quitting. While it takes about ten years from the time one stops smoking to achieve the health risk status of someone who has never smoked, most of the risk has disappeared within the first two years.

Blood Pressure

Your blood pressure is the pressure which is exerted on the walls of your blood vessels by your blood as it circulates through your body. The first (larger) number is called the 'systolic' pressure, and is a measure of the pressure in your arteries when your heart contracts. The second (smaller) number is called the 'diastolic' pressure, and is a measure of the pressure in your arteries between the heart beats. A blood pressure of 110/70 is read '110 over 70' and means 110 mm in a mercury column of systolic pressure and 70 mm in a mercury column of diastolic pressure.

Blood pressures greater than 140/90 are considered to be high, and steps should be taken to bring these figures down. In general, the lower the numbers the lower the risks of developing heart disease, atherosclerosis, stroke, or kidney damage. It should make sense that if your arteries are subjected to prolonged high pressures the risks are increased. The heart has to work harder, the artery walls tend to harden and narrow, and the tiny arteries in the kidneys are damaged, reducing that organ's ability to clear wastes from the blood.

High blood pressure does not have any symptoms associated with it, so many people who have it are unaware of their condition. In addition, since people with high blood pressure don't have further symptoms, and because the medications often create side effects, many people do not continue taking blood pressure reducing prescribed medication. Prevention is of course the best strategy, and if blood pressures do become chronically elevated, there are several natural lifestyle-related steps, outlined below which should be used.

If your blood pressure is elevated, there are several things you can do. First, you should get your blood pressure taken regularly. You can even take it yourself very easily – there are a number of accurate and inexpensive measurement devices available at any well-equipped local pharmacy. Second, if you are overweight, you may be able to reduce your blood pressure to 120/80 or below by simply losing weight. You should also watch your salt consumption very carefully – and remember that most of the salt we get comes from processed foods. And be sure to get plenty of exercise and build some kind of relaxation routine into your life; as both of these activities help to lower blood pressure. And finally, if these do not work, your doctor can prescribe medications which will lower your blood pressure.

Cholesterol and Triglycerides

Cholesterol and triglycerides are fatty substances produced in the body and carried in the blood stream. They are necessary for normal cell functioning. When they are produced in excessive quantities, they increase one's risk of developing heart disease. Cholesterol is increased by eating foods that contain saturated fats and/or cholesterol. Triglycerides are increased by eating foods high in sugar and by alcohol consumption. As with most biological processes, some people are more inclined to produce high levels of these substances than others.

Triglyceride levels respond very quickly, within a matter of days, to changes in sugar and alcohol intake. It is recommended that you keep your triglyceride level under 100 mg/dl. Many people have found that if their triglyceride level is elevated, it is difficult to alter one's cholesterol level through dietary changes.

Cholesterol's role in cardiovascular health has been extensively documented over the past few years. It is known that cholesterol levels are directly related to heart disease since excess cholesterol in the blood is deposited on the walls of arteries. When an artery that feeds the heart muscle becomes clogged, the result is a heart attack; when this happens in the brain, the result is a stroke.

Cholesterol travels through the blood stream in protein 'packets' called lipoproteins. Some of these packets are low density (LDL), and some are high density (HDL). The LDL form transports cholesterol from the liver into the rest of the body. This is the form of cholesterol which adheres to artery walls and causes problems. The HDL form transports cholesterol out of the body, and is now thought to be protective against heart attacks.

As a result of these different functions of the two forms of cholesterol, the current medical advice suggests that people reduce total and LDL cholesterol and increase HDL cholesterol. A diet low in saturated fats and cholesterol-rich foods will help to lower total (and LDL) cholesterol levels in most people. A regular vigorous exercise programme will increase the HDL portion. Thus a combination low fat/low cholesterol diet and a regular exercise programme are strongly suggested for protection or to reduce risk. Do you know what foods are high in saturated fats and cholesterol?

....

....

....

....

Saturated fats are those which are firm at room temperature (e.g. butter, cheese, beef and pork fat, coconut and palm 'oils'). A very common operation used by food manufacturers called 'hydrogenation' causes unsaturated oils (e.g. corn oil) to become more saturated. Cholesterol is concentrated in red meats (especially organ meats like kidney and liver) and in dairy products.

In addition to reducing the intake of foods rich in cholesterol and saturated fats, eating one third of a cup of oat bran or corn bran each day is a good natural way to reduce cholesterol. Niacin (nicotinic acid – a B vitamin) is a further way to reduce total cholesterol. A number of good books about cholesterol management are now available, and should be referred to for more detailed information.

Next Steps

If you have completed all the questionnaires you should now know what your scores mean in terms of risks to your health, your performance, and your general sense of well-being. If many of your scores were in the moderate to high risk areas, it is suggested that you set some priorities for yourself, and that you begin acting immediately to lower these risks. If nearly all of your scores were in the low risk area, congratulations! This would suggest that, at present, the pressures in your life and the lifestyle habits you have adopted are probably promoting good health, excellent performance and a positive sense of health and well-being.

This questionnaire package can only provide a 'snapshot' of your risks at a point in time. It is advisable to reassess your stress and lifestyle situation periodically, to ensure that you are keeping the risks at a safe low level. You should also keep in mind that this workbook is not intended to provide medical diagnosis. Its purpose is to provide you with some information and some risk estimations based on your responses. If several of your scores are in the high risk area, we suggest that you consult with your doctor or welfare officer to determine if there are any treatment measures called for.

Even if your overall rating was reasonable, there may well be some weak points which you would like to tackle. To do this we suggest that you set up an action plan, prioritise your goals and begin by working on just one goal at a time. This gradual approach to improvement has been shown repeatedly to lead to the best results over a period of years. The next section of the workbook will help you do this.

Personal Planning

This section may become the most important one in this workbook. We have found that if people don't begin to do something with the kinds of data contained in this workbook almost immediately, they tend never to get around to making the changes they might need to make to lower their health risks and improve their performance and sense of well-being. In other words, you need to take immediate action to get the ball rolling.

New Year's resolutions and other good intentions often don't reach a successful conclusion. There are generally two reasons for this. First, people often want to change too much at one time, and become overwhelmed and then give up. Second, the context for making the changes (e.g. January 2 or in the company lunch room) is often different from the context in which the resolutions were made (e.g. New Year's Eve or in a workshop).

Can you think of any occasions during the past six months when you have made resolutions or promises that you have not kept?

....

....

....

....

....

....

Think carefully for a few minutes and then jot down your thoughts on why all your good resolutions failed.

....

....

....

....

....

You will be more successful if you avoid attempting wholesale changes, and instead think about making one small change at a time. For example, start by not eating sweets during the week, or only smoking from 2 p.m. onwards. This way you will have successes rather than the failures that come with attempting to do too much too soon. With this approach, you will find that you are able to accumulate gradually significant amounts of change in a way that does not cause you to feel you are making great sacrifices. Those who are most successful at making personal changes are the people who accept that they are lifelong learners, and make changes one step at a time.

We suggest that you use the following worksheet to identify the possible projects you think you should eventually undertake, and then decide what your first project will be. This first project should be something that is manageable, something which you are confident you can succeed in accomplishing, and something you are committed to undertaking right away. Early successes create momentum which you can use when you come to the more difficult changes.

If you want to be most successful in taking charge of your life you must affirm that you are in charge and you must consciously choose to be healthy. When you do this, you vastly improve your chances of success. If you are unable to say to yourself in a strong and convincing way that you ARE in charge and that you CHOOSE to be healthy, it probably won't matter much what changes you attempt, since it is unlikely that you will realise the benefits of those changes.

In reviewing all the information you have gathered about your stress and strain levels and about your attitudes and lifestyle habits, please complete the following personal Action Plan.

Action Plan

The things I am doing well and want to maintain or continue are:

....

....

....

The things I need to stop doing or do less are:

....

....

....

The things I need to begin or do more are:

....

....

....

Now list these in order of priority:

....

....

....

Which one of these shall I undertake to do now or in the very near future?:

....

....

The first steps I plan to take are:

....

....

....

The factors that will hinder me are:

....

....

....

The factors that will help me are:

....

....

....

The implications of not acting are:

....

....

....

The kinds of support I will need are:

....

....

....

The agreements I need to make are:

....

....

....

I will know I have been successful when:

....

....

....

CONGRATULATIONS! You have now completed a quite thorough review of your stress and strain levels and those lifestyle factors which are most important for protecting and improving your health and performance. As you continue to follow-up on what you have learnt from your efforts you will find that you are increasingly satisfied with your life and that you are gaining more and more control over your responses to events as they arise.

Every effort has been made to make this package the most up-to-date and useful SELF SCORING stress and health assessment workbook available. If you have any questions or suggestions for improvement, please do not hesitate to contact us.

John D Adams PhD
Director
Eartheart Enterprises Inc
Route 5, Box 602
Winchester VA 22601
USA
703 665-9713

Lifeskills Communications Ltd
Wharfebank House
Ilkley Road, Otley
W. Yorks LS21 3JP
UK
0943-851144

Notes

Lifeskills

Personal Development Series

Other titles available in this series are:

ASSERTIVENESS

A Positive Process

'When we are assertive, we tell people what we want or need, or would prefer. We state our preferences clearly and confidently, without being aggressive, without belittling ourselves and without putting other people down.' Most of us are capable of being assertive, aggressive or unassertive at different times. The aim of this book is to help you benefit from the positive process of being assertive as consistently as you can. *Assertiveness, A Positive Process* will:

* help you to distinguish between assertive, aggressive and unassertive behaviour

* ensure that you understand the benefits of being assertive – and the dilemmas

* introduce you to some helpful techniques for dealing with people assertively

TRANSITIONS

The Challenge of Change

'When a chrysalis metamorphoses into a butterfly it is a natural process, it is something that must happen for the insect to become beautiful, to fly, to mate, to realise its potential.' This is a good symbol to use about facing our own transitions because we need to change to realise our potential. Change is essential, and creates opportunities, but it often causes stress and worry. Modern life is full of changes, the list is endless. *Transitions, the Challenge of Change* will:

* help you to identify the different types of transition and their patterns

* help you make sense of the confusing feelings you may experience after an upheaval

* emphasise the benefits that can come from transitions and provide a step-by-step, comprehensive guide to managing change positively

TIME MANAGEMENT

Conquer the Clock

Time Management is about recognising that time is limited, setting clear priorities and objectives for yourself, and then ensuring that you achieve them. *Time Management, Conquer the Clock* will:

* show you how to analyse your present use of time, including the concept of sold, maintenance and discretionary time

* help you identify the priorities in your life and rank them in order of importance

* introduce you to the many different ways and styles of managing time

COMMUNICATION

Time to Talk

'It is tempting to assume that our communication skills come to us as part of our natural development. Yet some people develop into very effective communicators, while others barely reach survival level...' Without communication there would be no relationships between people: sharing ideas, giving opinions, finding out what we need to know, working out differences, giving positive criticism and expressing our feelings are examples of the kind of face-to-face communication which is essential to our everyday life and work with other people. *Communication, Time to Talk* will:

* explain how to recognise and prevent 'communication breakdown' at work and at home

* help you to identify helpful and unhelpful ways of communicating

* encourage you to develop and improve your interpersonal communication skills

PREPARING FOR SUCCESSFUL LEARNING

More people are undertaking study programmes than ever before – courses range from full-time degrees and professional work-related courses to evening classes for pure enjoyment. By working through this book you will be able to assess and develop your attitude to study and your style of learning. How do you learn? What motivates you? Do you find it difficult to get down to it? We all have our individual learning styles and develop good and bad study habits. Part of the preparation for effective study is knowing ourselves and applying that knowledge to the way we work. *Preparing for Successful Learning* will help you:

* to identify your own learning style, its strengths and weaknesses

* to build on the strengths and strengthen the weaknesses of your style

* to identify your learning habits – good and bad – and make new ones

* to organise your learning, establish a routine and stick to a timetable

* to identify and overcome the barriers to getting started

SUCCESSFUL LEARNING IN ACTION

Good students are not born. No doubt some are born with intellectual gifts but many of the skills and techniques that go towards successful study can be learned. Once you have pre-pared yourself and you are ready to go, you need to know how to go about it. You also need to know how to use the knowledge you have gained to best effect. *Successful Learning in Action* is the second book on study skills and is full of information. It gives you comprehensive instructions on how to make the most of your study time. It also gives suggestions on how to present and use your study to best effect – both in written and in spoken form.

Successful Learning in Action aims to help students help themselves. It will enable you:

* to familiarise yourself with a range of study skills and learning techniques

* to develop your memory

* to make use of resources

* to make effective notes

* to write essays and reports

* to make speeches and give talks

* to do yourself justice in examinations

RELATIONSHIPS

A Question of Quality

Most of us would measure the quality of our lives not only by the extent of our personal achievements but by the quality of our relationships. Our lives would be empty without important relationships. Yet as with so many other key dimensions of our existence, relation-ships are so often taken for granted.

The workbook sets out:

* to explore why relationships are so vital to us

* to show that relationships do not just 'happen' – that you have to make them work

* to identify the skills needed to make, maintain and end relationships in a positive way

* to help you to be more aware of your skills and to develop them

* to help identify skills and strategies that will help you cope with relationships you find
  difficult

Other Mercury titles from Lifeskills are:

BUILD YOUR OWN RAINBOW

Barrie Hopson and Mike Scally

A Lifeskills Workbook for Career and Life Management
Adopted by the Open University for Work Choices, a Community Education course

Build Your Own Rainbow is the first of a new series of Lifeskills guides. It contains 40 exercises that will help answer the questions:

* who am I?
* where am I now?
* how satisfied am I?
* what changes do I want?
* how do I make them happen?
* what if it doesn't work out?

In the process of doing this, readers will discover what is important to them about work, where their main interests lie, what their transferable skills are and which career pattern would best suit them. They will be helped to set personal and career objectives, to make action plans and to take greater charge of their lives.

12 STEPS TO SUCCESS THROUGH SERVICE

Barrie Hopson and Mike Scally

A Lifeskills Management Guide

Satisfying the customer is the single most vital factor in business success and the main priority in any business must be to win and keep the customer. This book provides a complete programme to achieve success through service in twelve crucial steps:

* decide on your core business
* know your customer
* create your wisdom
* define your moments of truth
* give good service to one another
* manage the customer's experience
* profit from complaints
* stay close to your customer
* design and market the service programme
* set service criteria
* reward service excellence
* develop the service programme

Lifeskills is one of the leading providers of Quality Service Programmes in the English-speaking world.

POSITIVE LEADERSHIP

Mike Pegg

How to Build a Winning Team
A Lifeskills Management Guide

Good leaders have many features in common. They develop a clear vision, they inspire their people, gain commitment from them, then guide their teams to success. This sounds easy in theory but how is it done?

This is a book written for top teams, managers and anybody who is a leader of people. It offers a framework for leadership and teamwork, with concrete ideas which can be incorporated into the daily work plan.

It focuses on how to:

* provide positive leadership
* be a positive team member
* build a positive culture
* set a positive goal, and get commitment to reaching it
* be a positive implementer
* build a positive reputation
* get positive results
* continue to build a positive and successful team

CHANGING COURSE

Maggie Smith

A Workbook for Change and Reappraisal in Mid-life

Make the most of your opportunities and review your whole life at a time of change. This workbook is an invaluable resource and can be used by anyone undergoing a career change: whether this is a result of having been made redundant, having decided on taking early retirement, or simply because you are considering a change.

The workbook helps you to review subjects such as:

* what is work?
* money – how much do you really need?
* managing change
* time management
* work, paid and unpaid
* self employment
* stress management